Edited by Helen Exley

To my friend, Pam Brown.
Thank you for everything you've done to help
make this series what it is.

Acknowledgements: The publishers would like to thank the following
for permission to reprint copyright material. They would be pleased to
hear from any copyright holders not here acknowledged.

E. E. Cummings: The lines from "you shall above all things be glad
*and young." are reprinted from **Complete Poems, 1904-1962,** by*
E. E. Cummings, Edited by George J. Firmage, by permission of Liveright
Publishing Corporation and Grafton Books, now a division of
HarperCollins. Copyright © 1938, 1966, 1991 by the Trustees for the
E. E. Cummings Trust;

*Eleanor Farjeon: "Out Came the Sun" & "The Difference" from **The New***
***Book of Days,** published by Oxford University Press, reprinted by*
permission of David Higham Associates Ltd;

*Stephen Spender: "To My Daughter" from **Collected Poems 1928-1953***
*and **Selected Poems.** Copyright © 1955 Stephen Spender. Reprinted*
by permission of Faber & Faber Ltd, London and Random House, Inc.,
New York.

First published in Great Britain in 1990 by Exley Publications Ltd.
Published simultaneously in 1992 by Exley Publications Ltd in Great
Britain, and Exley Giftbooks in the USA.

12 11 10 9 8

Illustrations © Exley Publications Ltd, 1990
Selection & design © Helen Exley, 1990
Research by Pam Brown
ISBN 1-85015-235-7

Printed and bound in Spain by Grafo, S.A. – Bilbao.
Exley Publications Ltd, 16 Chalk Hill, Watford, Herts WD1 4BN, United Kingdom.
Exley Giftbooks, 232 Madison Avenue, Suite 1206, NY 10016, USA.

An illustrated

Girl's
Notebook

A personal journal for notes,
lists or private thoughts

EXLEY
NEW YORK · WATFORD, UK

Whatever you can do, or dream you can, begin it. Boldness has genius, power and magic in it.

Goethe

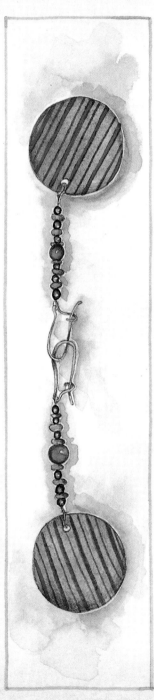

There are two sorts of girl. The one who feels
mournful that all eyes are on her. And the one
who is happily convinced that they are.
                                    Samantha Armstrong

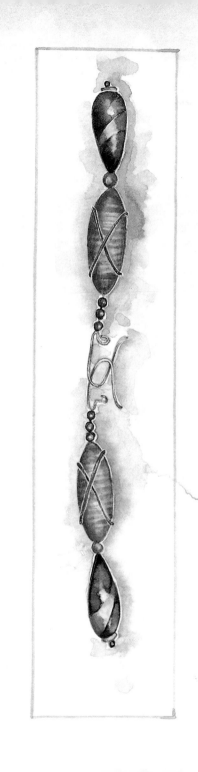

Stand firm in your refusal to remain conscious during Algebra. In real life, I assure you, there is no such thing as Algebra.

Fran Lebowitz

You have got to discover you, what you do, and trust it.
Barbra Striesand

I didn't belong as a kid, and that always bothered me. If only I'd known that one day my differentness would be an asset, then my early life would have been much easier.
Bette Midler

Everyone has their special gift. In some it is speech, in some, silence. The world has need of small perfections as well as great achievements.

Pam Brown

The world is made of people who never quite get into the first team and who just miss the prizes at the flower show.
J. Bronowski
from, "The Ascent of Man"

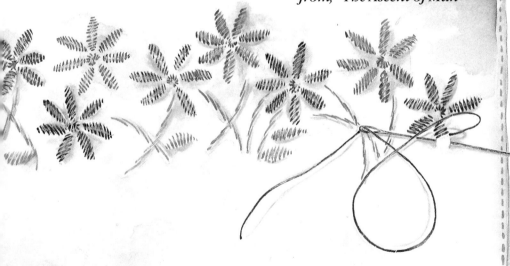

No one can make you feel inferior without your own consent.

Eleanor Roosevelt

Love is lunacy. What else would make me keep an empty tin of cola, a used Bandaid, a bus ticket and a bitten pencil stub.

Charlotte Gray

Forget-me-nots

for ~
· remembrance ·

⊱ Sage ⊰

~ symbolizes
mutual love ·

∞ Thyme ∞

~ symbolizes
Sweetness ~

Periwinkle

· for · ~ ·
happy memories

There are muddled kisses and clever kisses. The muddled ones are usually the ones you remember forever.
Samantha Armstrong

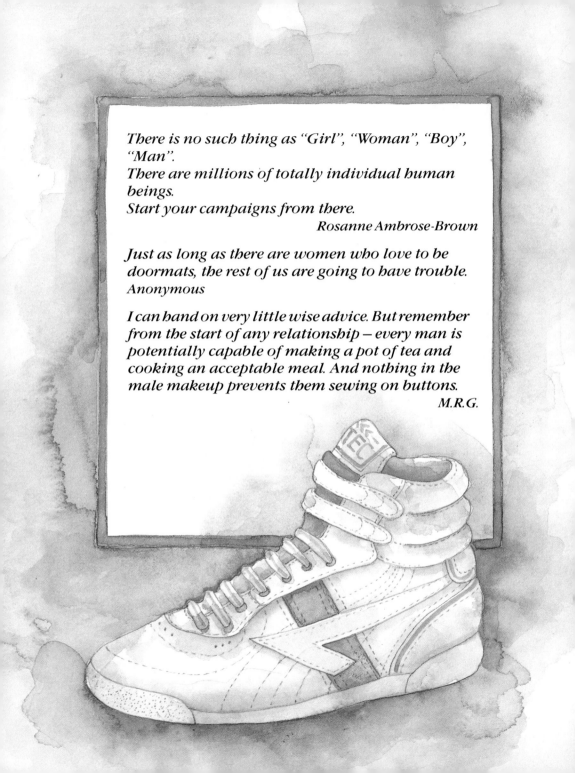

There is no such thing as "Girl", "Woman", "Boy", "Man".
There are millions of totally individual human beings.
Start your campaigns from there.
                        Rosanne Ambrose-Brown

Just as long as there are women who love to be doormats, the rest of us are going to have trouble.
Anonymous

I can hand on very little wise advice. But remember from the start of any relationship – every man is potentially capable of making a pot of tea and cooking an acceptable meal. And nothing in the male makeup prevents them sewing on buttons.
                        M.R.G.

Out came the sun
And out came the dresses
Girls every one
From tissue recesses
Pulled out the new frock
The yellow, the pink,
The lavender-blue frock
And all in a twink
Each one had got on
Her muslin or cotton,
Going all gay on
Gingham and rayon,
Golden as sunlight,
Clear as the sky
White as the wisp
Of the cloud floating by;
All clean and crisp
They come in the hour
Of the one light
That opens the heat of the flower
Girls in their summer gowns
Patterned and plain,
Girls in green dots
And rose-coloured spots
Girls like the rainbow that follows the rain
Brightened the streets of the cities again.

Eleanor Farjeon
from "The New Book of Days"

Young people do not know enough to be prudent, and therefore they attempt the impossible – and achieve it, generation after generation.

Pearl Buck
from "The Goddess Abides"

There is no need to do any housework at all. After the first four years the dirt doesn't get any worse.

Quentin Crisp

In a world that seems dominated by greed and selfishness and cruelty, there are always enough people sitting on pavements, carrying banners, picketting embassies, signing petitions, making speeches, cornering politicians and setting up organisations to give the heart a little hope.

Pam Brown

Daughters are not the chance to do a corrective re-run on one's own misguided youth. They want their own misguided youth.

Pam Brown

Just when the world seems chained forever in dark and cold, up bobs the next generation, brash and bright as daffodils.

Helen Thomson

*Oh, the comfort, the inexpressable comfort of
feeling safe with a person, having neither to
weigh thoughts nor measure words, but
pouring them right out, just as they are, chaff
and grain together, certain that a faithful hand
will take and sift them, keep what is worth
keeping, and then with the breath of kindness,
throw the rest away.*

*Dina Maria Mulock
from "A Life for a Life"*

Why not be oneself? That is the whole secret of a successful appearance. If one is a greyhound, why try to look like a Pekinese?

Edith Sitwell

You can take no credit for beauty at sixteen. But if you are beautiful at 60, it will be your own soul's doing.

Marie Stopes

Taking joy in life is a woman's best cosmetic.

Rosalind Russell

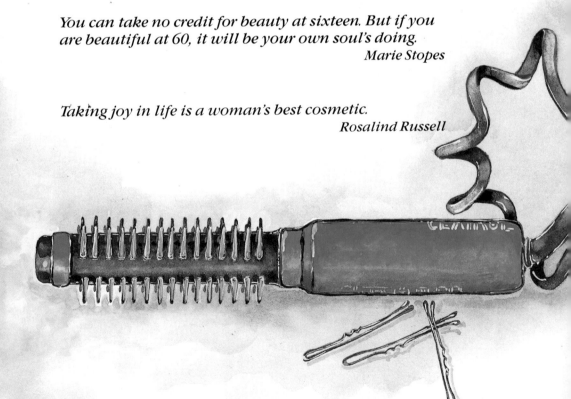

You shall above all things be glad and young
for if you're young, whatever life you wear

it will become you; and if you are glad
whatever's living will yourself become

e.e. cummings

No woman can call herself free who does not own and control her own body.

Margaret Sanger

No one is "free". That would be to live in total isolation. We are woven into every other life and must recognise this fact if the planet is to survive.

Peter Gray

An adult woman is one who does not think predominantly of her sex, but of her humanity.

W. C. Faith

Examinations are passed on coffee, toffees, peanuts and bacon butties. It is hard to possess both a finely honed mind and a finely honed body.

Patricia Hitchcock

I think this thing is love

I have manufactured love, to seem the same,
and sighed about the corridors, written a name
all round the edges of "Decline and Fall"
and lied a little in the dining hall;
but now, without warning or intent, I find
this awkward, silent boy invades my mind

Unwillingly I search the street
for him. By calculated chance we meet,
by accidental certainty we go
the same way home, and drift and slow
and listen for the other; scarcely talk
all through the blurred, familiar walk.

There is no permanence in this;
the surreptitious touching of the hands, the kiss
— no more than their encounters. There will be
other concerns for him, for me.
We've got things to learn and things to prove.
And yet,
        I know that this is love.

Pam Brown

Success is not fame or money or the power to bewitch. It is to have created something valuable from your own individuality and skill — a garden, an embroidery, a painting, a cake. A life.

Charlotte Gray

Some boys say it with flowers, some with chocolate, some with perfume. But the best present is some oddity you mentioned in passing, that you liked and he's spent three lunch times searching for.

Susan Millard

To My Daughter
Bright clasp of her white hand around my finger.
My daughter, as we walk together now,
All my life I'll feel a ring invisibly
Circles this bone with shining: when she is grown
Far from today as her eyes are far already.
                                   Stephen Spender

*Twenty-four hours can transform something you can't
live without into second rate trash.
This goes for boys and dresses.*

Patricia Hitchcock

Inside every slim, beautiful girl, is a fat, middle-aged woman waiting to get out.

Samantha Armstrong

Sunburn is very becoming — but only when it is even — one must be careful not to look like a mixed grill.

*Noel Coward
from "The Lido Beach"*

The models of bras in catalogues should be banned. They send every normal female into a deep depression.

Pam Brown

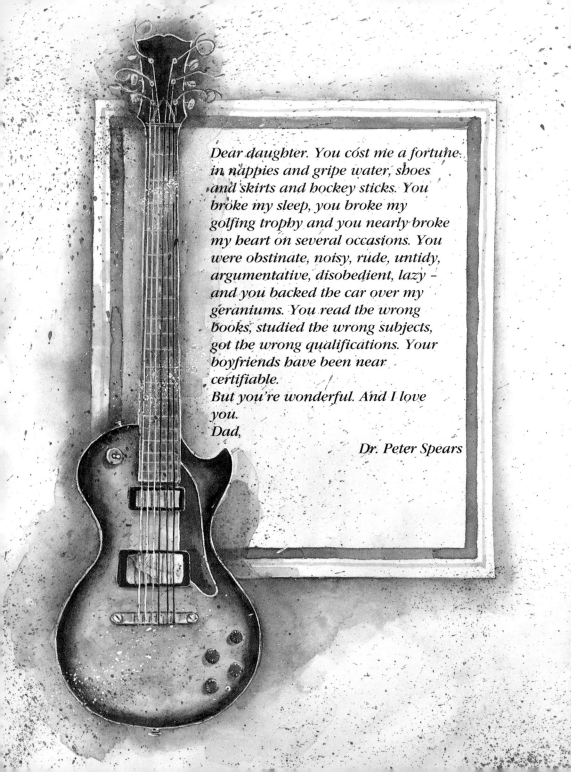

Dear daughter. You cost me a fortune in nappies and gripe water, shoes and skirts and hockey sticks. You broke my sleep, you broke my golfing trophy and you nearly broke my heart on several occasions. You were obstinate, noisy, rude, untidy, argumentative, disobedient, lazy – and you backed the car over my geraniums. You read the wrong books, studied the wrong subjects, got the wrong qualifications. Your boyfriends have been near certifiable.

But you're wonderful. And I love you.

Dad.

Dr. Peter Spears

Become a true expert in something. Anything. Then the question of you being a woman will barely raise its head.

Dr. Janine Cooper

Macho male dancers, gentle male nurses, dominant female Prime Ministers, gutsy female archaeologists. At last — a world where it's ability that counts, not sex. We're not there yet — but watch this space. . . .

Pam Brown

I refuse to consign the whole male sex to the nursery. I insist on believing that some men are my equals.

Brigid Brophy

I'm furious about the Women's Liberationists. They keep getting up on soapboxes and proclaiming that women are brighter than men. That's true, but it should be kept very quiet or it ruins the whole racket.

from "The Observer" Sayings of the Year

The Difference

Your eye may see
And your ear may hear
What the eye of a bee
Or a rabbit's ear
Are looking at and listening to
Every day of the year, like you.

But the rabbit's ear
Will never hear more
Than it heard last year
And the year before;
And the honey-bee's eyes see no new thing
As it looks on the garden from spring to spring

But while you grow,
And as you change,
You will come to know
New meanings strange
In the things you listen to, said or sung,
And the things you're looking at now you're young.

That, my dear,
Is one reason why,
With your little ear,
And your little eye,
You are quite unlike the rabbit and bee
Who never can change what they hear and see.

Eleanor Farjeon
from "A New Book of Days

Coffee in the kitchen, shoeless and exhausted after a hard day's shopping, patches up a multitude of difference between a daughter and her mum.

Pam Brown

Never grow a wishbone, daughter,
Where your backbone ought to be.

Clementine Paddleford

The way you overcome shyness is to become so wrapped up in something that you forget to be afraid.

Lady Bird Johnson

It's wonderful to be looked after — but it's even more wonderful to be able to look after yourself.

Jesse O'Neill

If at first you don't succeed, try again. Then quit. No use being a damn fool about it.
W.C. Fields

Only good girls keep diaries. Bad girls don't have the time.

Tallulah Bankhead

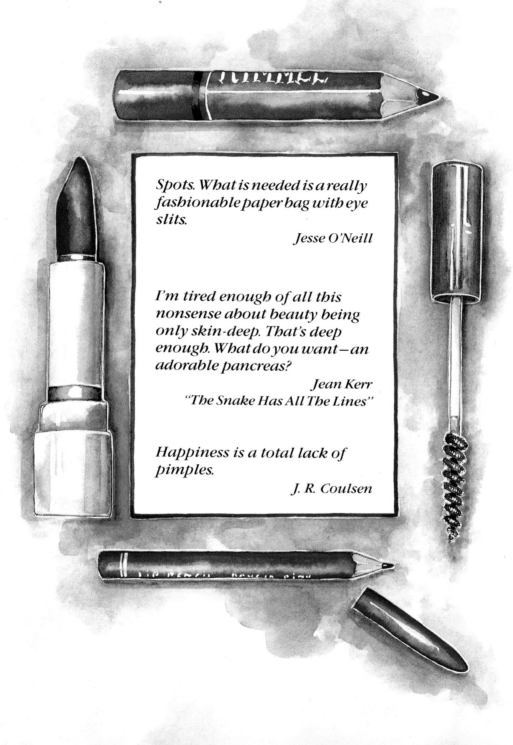

Spots. What is needed is a really fashionable paper bag with eye slits.

Jesse O'Neill

I'm tired enough of all this nonsense about beauty being only skin-deep. That's deep enough. What do you want—an adorable pancreas?

Jean Kerr
"The Snake Has All The Lines"

Happiness is a total lack of pimples.

J. R. Coulsen

When your friend holds you
affectionately by both hands
you are safe, for you can watch
both of his.

               Ambrose Bierce

Love is walking two miles
out of your way just
to pass his gate. Even if
you know he's not there.
Samantha Armstrong

For the first time in the history of the world, the fashion is simply to be yourself; go for it!
Sally Edith Benjamin

Why does the most vital learning period of one's life coincide with a blinding obsession with the opposite sex?

M.R.G.

I never hated a man enough to give him his diamonds back.

Zsa Zsa Gabor

Sex is only the liquid centre of the great Newberry Fruit of friendship.

Jilly Cooper

As long as femininity is associated with ruffles and flourishes and a lack of directness and honesty . . . (women) are never praised without being patronised. Their jacket photographs are reviewed instead of their books.

Erica Jong

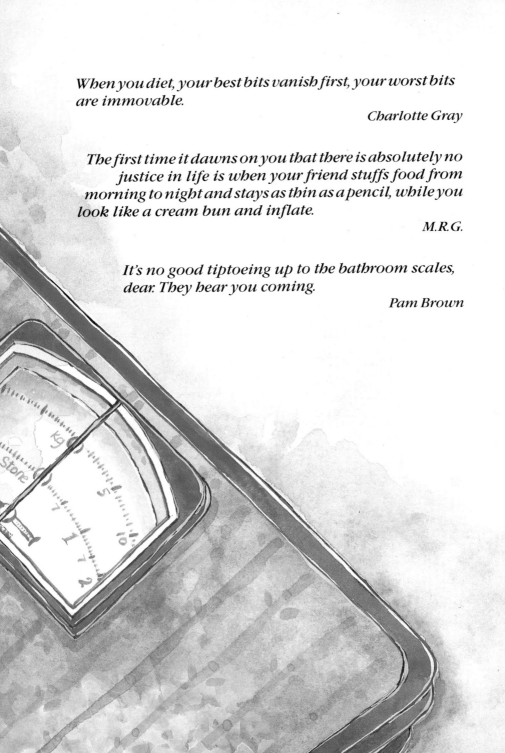

When you diet, your best bits vanish first, your worst bits are immovable.

Charlotte Gray

The first time it dawns on you that there is absolutely no justice in life is when your friend stuffs food from morning to night and stays as thin as a pencil, while you look like a cream bun and inflate.

M.R.G.

It's no good tiptoeing up to the bathroom scales, dear. They hear you coming.

Pam Brown

My dear, I wish you love and beauty, joy and excitement, discovery, achievement and that inner stillness which is peace of mind. I wish I could pass on to you the pleasures the years have given me. Books. Pictures. Music. Places. But you have your own wonders waiting for you. I wish I could go with you — but this is your adventure. Remember me.

Pam Brown

Daughters never give their mothers enough credit — and if they don't, no one else damn well will.

Jane Swan

Wherever you go you'll find your mum has packed layers of love in your baggage.

Helen Thomson

*It is astonishing
how many young people embark upon
life with a teddy bear at the bottom of
their trunk.*
Pam Brown

The purpose of life, after all, is to live it, to taste experience to the utmost, to reach out eagerly and without fear for newer and richer experience.

Eleanor Roosevelt

Everyone in the world has something unique to offer. Everyone.

H.M.E.

Mistakes are necessary. Embarrassment is necessary. How else can we learn? How else can we discover the necessities of patience, kindness, sympathy and forgiveness?

Clara Ortega

If you can react the same way to winning and losing, that's a big accomplishment.

Chris Evert

Risk! Risk anything! Care no more for the opinions of others, for those voices. Do the hardest thing on earth for you. Act for yourself. Face the truth.

Katherine Mansfield

You will do foolish things,
but do them with enthusiasm.
                    Colette